Total Trauma!

Really Embarrassing Stories

By
Rebecca Gómez

Copyright © 2001 Kidsbooks, Inc.
230 Fifth Avenue
New York, NY 10001

Manufactured in Canada

Visit us at **www.kidsbooks.com.**
Volume discounts available for group purchases.

Introduction

Trauma Time!

Have you ever had a totally embarrassing moment? One of those times when you turned bright red, felt your stomach drop, and wanted to sink into the floor and disappear? You're not alone!

All of us, at one time or another, have done something so humiliating and stupid that we swore we'd never show our face in public again. All of us have lived through the horror to tell the tale.

"Oh, sure," you're probably thinking. "Nothing could be worse than the total trauma *I've* endured!" Chances are, no matter what happened to you, something very much like it happened to someone else, somewhere nearby.

So whether you're looking for blushing companionship or just for a few laughs, read on to see just how embarrassing life can be!

Chapter One

Why Me?

Does it sometimes seem as though humiliating things happen only to you? Do you ever find yourself wondering how your big sister or best friend manages to avoid mortifying moments? Or how you happen to find yourself in the wrong place, at the wrong time, so much of the time? Here's a sampling of some classic "Why Me?" stories. Read them and you'll see that you're not alone. How many have *you* experienced?

You Smell Good

I love perfumes and lotions. One afternoon, I was at the local pharmacy looking for a new moisturizer. I was walking down the aisle, sniffing each lotion and trying to decide which one I wanted to buy. Suddenly, I heard someone call my name. I turned around and saw my crush right behind me. Not wanting to look like a total dweeb, I quickly put the lotion that I'd been sniffing back on the shelf. But I didn't put it all the way back, and it started to tip over. I quickly caught it, but the cap was still open— and the lotion squirted right into my face! By the time I'd cleaned myself up, my crush's face was red from laughing so hard. My own face was red—from utter humiliation!

—Breanne

An Extra Pair

One morning before school, I couldn't find anything to wear. I was in a big rush, so I just grabbed a pair of jeans from a pile of clean clothes in the laundry room. I didn't even look in the mirror once I was dressed—I just ran out of the house to catch the bus. Once I got to school, I chatted with some friends before the homeroom bell rang. One of my pals came up from behind me and started cracking up. "Aren't you supposed to wear those on the *inside*?" she said, as she pointed at the back of my pants. Horrified, I reached back and felt a pair of underpants sticking out from my back pocket! I was so embarrassed, I grabbed the underpants, stuffed them in my locker, and took off for homeroom. Why do these things always happen to me?

—Heidi

Instant Message Mishap

I am still asking myself how I let this happen. One night, I was at home surfing the Internet when an instant message popped up on my monitor. I didn't recognize the screen name, so I asked who the message was from. The answer came back that it was Lori, a friend of mine from school. So we started chatting back and forth, talking about boys. "Lori" asked me who I liked and I told her, but only after she promised not to tell anyone. The next day at school, I saw Lori and reminded her about her promise. She, of course, had no idea what I was talking about.

It turns out my correspondent was not Lori, but the best friend of my crush—who told everyone in school my secret!

—Betsy

Speech, Speech!

I was running for class secretary and had to make a speech in front of the entire school. I was really nervous because I had never spoken in front of such a large group of people before. There were four candidates running, and I was the second to speak. When it was my turn, I mustered up all of my courage and climbed up on the stage. Just as I got to the microphone, I let out a *huge* sneeze. It was so loud that there was feedback from the microphone for at least a few seconds. I was so embarrassed, I barely made it through my speech. I hurried back down to my seat the minute it was over. I thought the humiliation was over, but then the candidate after me made a point of wiping off the microphone with a big tissue. Of all moments, why did my body have to pick this one to sneeze?

—Dana

Beyond Britney

For our school's talent show last year, two of my friends and I decided to dance and lip-sync to a Britney Spears song. We rehearsed every day after school until we had the routine down perfectly. Finally, the big night came. When it was our turn to perform, we got up on stage and started to dance. But somehow, in all the excitement, I miscounted and thought the singing started earlier than it really did. I opened up my mouth and started singing before my cue. We were only supposed to lip-sync, so I wasn't singing loudly, but the microphones picked up my voice anyway. My friends stopped dancing and stared at me, and everyone in the auditorium started laughing. It was horrible! I still blush every time I hear that Britney Spears song.

—Pat

The Nose Knows

I was sitting with a bunch of my friends in the cafeteria. My buds and I were having a good time, telling jokes and laughing. One of my friends told this really funny joke just as I was drinking my soda. I swear this has never happened to me before, but I was laughing so hard that the soda started pouring out of my nose! I had no control as the liquid poured out of my nostrils. I almost died of embarrassment, especially when I looked over and saw that the kids at the next table were cracking up. It was a nightmare!

—Rachel

Overheard

I love to sing, and I often perform solos in school plays. I have a little routine that I always follow before I sing—I find a quiet spot and make "oooh" and "ahhhhh" noises with my mouth. I know I sound silly, but it really helps to calm my nerves and relax my voice. Last year, I signed up to be in our school's talent show. It was really busy and crowded backstage, so I went off to a remote hallway to do my voice exercises. There I was, "ooohing" and "ahhhhing," when suddenly I heard someone clear his throat. I looked up to see this really cute guy staring right at me! I hadn't realized that the "remote" hallway I'd chosen was right in front of the restrooms. I felt like such a dork!

—Shawna

Don't Fence Me In

One day after school, I got a ride home from my friend's mom. She was driving a whole bunch of us home, including this totally cute guy from my math class. I got to sit next to him during the ride, and we talked the entire time. It was awesome—I felt that I made a really good impression on him. But that all changed when we got to my stop! I got out of the car and turned around to thank my friend's mom and wave good-bye. Then, when I turned back around, I walked right smack into our front-yard fence! Everyone in the car started to giggle and I was so embarrassed I just ran inside. It was a humiliating moment that I'll never forget!

—Nancy

Chapter Two

School Daze

How many of your most awful moments happened during the school day? Maybe it's because so much time is spent there, but embarrassing things always seem to happen to students at school. Whether it's in the locker room, the cafeteria, the classroom, or on the playground, mixing together a group of energetic kids can be a recipe for disaster!

Food Fight!

I may never go into our school cafeteria again! Last week, a bunch of boys started a food fight. At first they were just throwing stuff back and forth at their own table. But before long, somebody at another table got hit, and food began flying everywhere. I didn't want to get filthy, so I tried to sneak out of the side door. Just as I was about to escape, I heard someone call my name. I turned around to see my friend, Jared, running toward me with his hand in the air. He smashed a cherry tomato on my head! I didn't know what to do. Our school doesn't have showers, so I wasn't going to be able to wash it out. Finally, one of my friends saw me, walked me to the girls' bathroom, and helped me comb some of that tomato out of my hair. I had to spend the rest of my day smelling like spaghetti sauce. All my friends called me "Marianna Marinara!"

—Marianna

Jell-O Jam

One day during lunch, I was feeling hyper and started swinging my lunch bag around over my head (I think I had had too much sugar). After a few seconds, I heard screams from the table behind me. When I turned around, I saw that a Jell-O pack had flown out of my bag and onto the table behind me. The people sitting at the table were covered in green Jell-O—and pretty annoyed with me!

—Linda

Fumble!

This is almost too embarrassing to repeat! We were playing a game of coed flag football at school. I'd worn an old pair of shorts; the elastic was wearing out and they fit rather loosely around my waist. I was running down the field when I felt a really hard tug and sensed my shorts slipping down. Someone on the other team had gotten a little too enthusiastic and had pulled on my shorts instead of the flag! When I stopped running, my shorts were around my knees and the whole class was laughing.

—Jane

Splat!

One rainy Thursday afternoon after choir rehearsal, I was standing on the school steps with some friends, waiting for my dad to pick me up. He's usually on time, but that day he was late, and I was getting wet. Eventually, a small green car—one that looked just like ours—pulled into the school parking lot. I ran over to the car, but just as I was about to open the passenger-side door, I tripped and fell into a huge puddle. I got totally soaked and, the worst part was, it wasn't even my dad's car! All my friends—and the stranger in the car—were cracking up. It was totally humiliating!

—Mary

The Show Must Go On

I had scored the lead role in our school play. Everything ran smoothly on opening night—until my final scene, that is. I'd ended up kneeling on the floor, just as I was supposed to (it was a dance number). When I got up, however, my heel got caught in the hem of my long dress. I didn't realize this until I was on my feet, and by then it was too late. I looked down to see that the bottom half of my skirt had torn off, leaving my legs bare from mid-thigh down. I didn't want to let the drama teacher down, so I just pretended that it was supposed to happen and finished the scene. My teacher thought I was a trouper for going on with the show, but I was as embarrassed as could be!

—Trudy

Band Aid

I play the piccolo in our school's marching band. We perform at town parades and during the half-time show of every home football game. We play without sheet music and do pretty intricate marching drills, so there's a lot of rehearsal involved. Last fall, I was sick and missed two weeks of practice before the big homecoming game. Needless to say, I was feeling less than confident about the performance. I had good reason! Halfway into the number, I turned left when I should have turned right. I started marching in the wrong direction, all by myself! I was concentrating so hard on playing the correct notes that it wasn't until the whole crowd started laughing that I realized my mistake. When I turned around, the rest of the band was half a football field away from me!

—Keri

Busted!

I really wish this hadn't happened to me! One day I was passing notes in class with a friend. We both knew we shouldn't be doing it, but we had a substitute teacher and were pretty sure she wouldn't notice. Boy, were we wrong! Not only did we get caught, but the teacher read our note aloud to the entire class! The worst part was, I had written all about this boy I like, who was sitting in the row right behind me! Everyone in the class laughed—except my crush. He turned bright red, just like me.

—Brandi

Life's a Stage

I was really psyched for our spring play last year. We were performing

The Wizard of Oz and I had won the role of Dorothy. I'd practiced really hard, memorized all of my lines, and felt confident about my performance. But on the night of the show, I started to get nervous. I decided to do some voice exercises to calm myself down. I start singing little songs and jingles and nursery rhymes—anything to keep my voice loose and flexible. Imagine my embarrassment when our drama teacher came running backstage, looking for whoever was "making all that racket." It seems that the AV team had turned the mikes on early, and the entire auditorium could hear me! I was almost too humiliated to go on stage, but the show must go on, right?

—Susan

Double Talk

One day, I was at a school assembly about environmental issues. Toward the end of the assembly, the speaker started taking questions. I had one, so I raised my hand. "Okay," the speaker said. "You in the green shirt." I assumed the speaker was calling on me—I *was* wearing a green shirt, after all. It wasn't until I started speaking that I realized the kid in front of me was also wearing green, and he was the one who had been called on! It was totally embarrassing—especially since the teacher sitting in my row started scolding me for talking out of turn!

—Shira

Chapter Three

Close Calls

Everyone has had moments that they wish they could do over. But sometimes an incident is not just humiliating, it's downright dangerous! The kids in the following stories almost had more than their pride hurt. Don't worry, though: no one was actually harmed during these episodes, just really, really embarrassed! Check out the following stories and see if you can relate.

Pride-breaker

I snuck a jawbreaker into my mouth at the beginning of math class. Needless to say, we are not allowed to eat candy in class. One of my friends whispered a joke to me and I started to laugh really hard. Before I knew it, I'd half-swallowed that jawbreaker. I couldn't catch my breath and I started pounding on my desk. My math teacher rushed over and started to give me the Heimlich maneuver. When she finally dislodged the jaw-breaker, it went flying out of my mouth and hit my friend, who sits directly across from me. The whole class started cracking up. Not only was I was bright red, but my teacher gave me detention for eating candy in class!

—Sara

Hot Head

My best friend and I were working together in science lab. We are usually very careful with the chemicals and the Bunsen burner, but clearly we were not careful enough on this day. Halfway through the lab, we noticed a really funny smell. Then my partner screamed, "It's your hair!" Luckily, only one strand had caught fire and I managed to put it out right away. But my embarrassment was not extinguished so quickly—everyone started calling me "Hot Head," and the smell of burned hair stayed with me all day long!

—Deborah

Danger on the Playground

One day after school, I was hanging out with my older brother and some of his friends at the park. One of them offered to spin me on the twirl-around in the playground. I usually don't like rides that spin—but I didn't want this guy to think I was lame. So even though my stomach is not very strong, I agreed. Big mistake! He started twirling me really fast and I started to feel really sick. Then, just as it was slowing down—and he was reaching out to help me off—I totally lost it and threw up all over him. It was so disgusting.

—Serena

Hot Stuff

One night I was out to dinner with my family, celebrating my big sister's graduation. A couple of my sister's way-cool friends were there, too. We were at a local restaurant and had ordered chicken fingers as an appetizer. The chicken came with several different sauces: There was sweet and sour, honey mustard, barbecue, and hot mustard. I took a piece of chicken and almost drowned it in the honey mustard—at least, what I thought was the honey mustard. I crammed the whole thing into my mouth and realized, a few seconds too late, that it was the hot mustard! I started coughing and my eyes started watering and I was forced to spit the chicken out onto my plate. It was totally disgusting, but what could I do? Everyone at the table cracked up, and I was truly mortified!

—Kathryn

Doggone It!

It was a Saturday afternoon and my mom had asked me to take the dog out for a walk. It was a gorgeous day, so I decided to combine this chore with one of my favorite activities— in-line skating. Bad idea! I put on my skates, hooked Mitzy up to her leash, and went to the park. Everything went smoothly for about 15 minutes, until a loud car horn startled Mitzy. The next thing I knew, she was tearing down the street, pulling me along with her! I tried to get control of the situation but failed: She ended up running me into the low wooden fence around our house—and tangling me up in her leash! When I finally got to my feet and unwound the leash from around my legs, I noticed my neighbors rushing over to see if I was okay. Once they saw that I was, they all started cracking up!

—Pam

Flying Through the Air

I was sitting on a bench in our school gym, waiting for a basketball game to start. I noticed that the bench was not very sturdy when I first sat down, but I didn't think anything of it. I wish I had, because when the coach—who was obviously much heavier than me—sat on the other end of the bench, the side I was sitting on went up and I flew right off! Fortunately, there were gymnastic mats spread near where I'd been sitting. Unfortunately, the entire basketball team saw what happened!

—Lucy

Chapter Four

On the Home Front

You might think that you are safe from embarrassing moments when you are with your family. Think again! These are the people who know you best, and who know exactly what makes you blush. You may be protected from harm in your household, but you're never too far from a humiliating incident!

Late, Again!

I'm a very on-time person. Unfortunately, I didn't inherit this trait from my parents—they're late for everything! A couple of weeks ago, my Girl Scout troop had an awards presentation. A couple of my friends and I were being presented with an award for a project that we'd just completed. The presentation started at 7 p.m. When I walked in with my family in tow—at 7:20—I had missed it entirely. The real humiliation began when my troop leader, who was standing in front of the audience, said very loudly, "Oh, Lily, so nice of you to make it. Too bad you missed the award!" My parents felt bad and tried to make it up to me, but I was so embarrassed!

—Lily

Dancing Queen

We moved into a new house about two weeks ago. Last Saturday afternoon, I happened to be home alone. I decided to take advantage of the empty living room and have a solo dance party. I cranked up the stereo really loud and started dancing all around the room. I got totally into it and really went wild! After about 15 minutes, I heard some loud knocking. At first I couldn't figure out where it was coming from. Eventually, I looked out the big picture window in the living room and saw three cute guys from the neighborhood—waving at me with big smiles on their faces. They'd seen my whole dance routine! I was truly mortified!

—Teresa

Sandbox Scare

I have a little brother who is two years old. One Saturday afternoon, I decided to give my mom a break and take him to the playground. When we arrived, it was very crowded, but no one was in the sandbox, so I took him there to play. For some reason, my brother was scared of the sand. Something about the texture bothered him. But I didn't want to take him home just yet, so I tried to encourage him to play in the sandbox. I took his plastic shovel and pail, climbed in, sat down, and started tossing sand around. To show him how much fun I was having, I really exaggerated and played it up. All of a sudden, I heard some kids laughing. I looked up to see that a bunch of kids from my school were standing just outside the playground, watching me. I must have looked like a total loser! The only good thing is that I helped my brother get over his fear of sandboxes. But my face is still red!

—Sandra

Kris/Chris

One night after school, I'd finished all my homework and was just hanging out watching television. When the telephone rang, my mom answered it. She walked into the living room, handed me the phone, and announced that it was Kris. I assumed that was Kris, as in Kristina, my best friend. Earlier that day we had been goofing around, talking to each other in silly accents. I took the phone and, without giving her a chance to speak, starting talking in a very heavy—and phony—

British accent. When I finished my sentence, there was complete silence on the other end of the phone. Then I heard this familiar *male* voice, say, "Uh, Sylvie? This is Chris." It was Chris, a boy from my science class, not Kris, my best friend! I was so embarrassed, and Chris thought I was nuts!

—Sylvie

If It Acts Like a Dog...

My little sister is crazy about dogs. We don't own one, but she's constantly asking my parents if she can have a puppy. One afternoon, the two of us were in the backyard playing her favorite game—"I've got a puppy." As usual, I played the part of the puppy. (Aren't I such a good big sis?) I was barking and whimpering and licking her face, when I heard someone laughing. I looked over our backyard fence and saw our next-door neighbor (who I happen to think is totally cute) sitting on his back steps. He could see right over our fence and into our backyard, and he was watching me act like a puppy for my little sister! I turned bright red and ran into our house!

—Donna

Lambie

My name is Lee Ann, but my family nickname has always been Lambie. My younger brother gave it to me—when he was little he couldn't pronounce Lee Ann, so he called me Lambie. The name stuck. One day a few weeks ago, my mom offered to drive me to school. It was a gorgeous morning, so she had the top down on her convertible. We pulled into the school parking lot, where a bunch of my friends were standing. As I was getting out of the car, my mom called out loudly, "Have a good day, Lambie!" She drove off before she realized what she'd done (she apologized later), but everyone on the steps heard her, and I was mortified! Now everyone at school calls me Lambie!

—Lee Ann

Mama Trauma

One day during lunch my friend and I traded sandwiches. I really wish I had unwrapped it first, because my mom had put a little note in it which said, "I love you, sweet pea!" My friend showed it to everyone—it was awful!

—Sheri

Chapter Five

Klutzy Chaos!

Have you ever had an embarrassing moment that made you feel like the biggest klutz on Earth? Have you ever been in an awkward situation that seemed to get progressively worse as the seconds flew by? The kids in the following stories sure have—and survived horrendous humiliation to tell their tales!

Knockout!

This was the worst! I was at the movies with a few of my friends. On our way out of the theater, I noticed that a few of my older brother's friends were right behind us. I have a total crush on one of them, so I got really nervous and preoccupied when I saw them. I turned around really quickly and, because I wasn't paying attention, ended up missing the door and walking right into the wall! I was stunned and slid to the floor. Then, as if I wasn't already humiliated enough, one of the guys recognized me. I was trying to act cool, so I jumped to my feet—just as he was bending over to help me. In my rush, I ended up smashing my head into his nose, giving him a huge nosebleed! I was so embarrassed that I didn't even ask him

if he was okay—I just fled the scene
as fast as I could!

—Jean

The Queen of Drool

One Saturday afternoon, my best
friend and I went to the local candy
shop to buy a couple of slushies. As we
were walking home, we ran into my
friend's older sister. She's really cool and
I totally look up to her. She's also really
nice to me, and she gave me a big hug
when we were saying good-bye.
Unfortunately, I had just taken a huge
sip of slushy right before she did, and I
accidentally drooled red liquid all over
the back of her shirt! If that wasn't bad
enough, I got so flustered when I realized what I had done that I swallowed
the wrong way and started coughing

uncontrollably. My friend's sister was really nice about the whole thing, but I never felt so stupid in my whole life!

—Kimberly

Dangerous Instruments

I just started playing the tuba in our school marching band. I've gotten pretty good at hitting all the right notes, but keeping the huge, heavy instrument in my control is another story! One day during rehearsal, I was having a particularly hard time with the thing. Halfway through our marching routine, the instrument started to feel *really* heavy. Eventually, it got to be too much and I started to fall out of sync with the other marchers. I bumped into the drummer and then over I went! Everyone in the band started cracking up. I was incredibly embarrassed and decided to learn the flute, instead!

—Marita

Movie Madness

One night I was at the movies with my mom. We had already settled into our seats when I realized that I had to go to the bathroom. I whispered that I'd be right back and headed to the ladies' room. As usual, there was a long line. By the time I got back, the lights were down and the movie had already started. I rushed down the aisle and plopped into my seat. Without thinking, I reached over and grabbed some of the popcorn that we'd bought. There was a gasp and the person next to me said, "Excuse me!" When I looked over, I realized that I'd sat in the wrong row—and taken some strange woman's popcorn! I was so embarrassed that I stood up, blocking the view of the person behind me. "Sit down!" he said loudly. I didn't know what to do so I dashed out of the theater. After I had collected myself, I went back in and did not sit down until I was sure I had spotted my mother. "What took you so long?" she asked.

—Linda

Kick Ball

It's one thing to accidentally kick a soccer ball in the wrong direction. But what I did was even worse—I missed the ball entirely! I was running to make a goal, missed the ball, then fell smack on my butt. It was terrible!

—Annabeth

Slipup

I was graduating from junior high school and the auditorium floor had just been waxed. The teachers had warned us not to walk too fast while we were marching in because the floor was very slippery. I was so nervous that I would slip, and—of course—I did! Just as I was walking up to the podium, I hit a slick spot and down I went. But that wasn't all. When I got up, I immediately hit another slippery spot and fell again. Everyone cracked up. It was so embarrassing.

—Karen

Jump-rope Jam

I was jumping rope with some friends during recess. I am usually really good at jump rope, but for some reason

I felt totally uncoordinated on this day. There were a group of cute guys watching us, and I just knew I would embarrass myself if I kept jumping, so I offered to swing the rope instead. Unfortunately, that didn't stop an embarrassing moment from occurring! After swinging for about four or five minutes, the girl holding the other end of the rope accidentally let it go! It went flying into my face and got curled all around me. Luckily I didn't get hurt, but everyone around me found it very amusing!

—Carol

Report Problems

I was giving an oral report in front of my class one day. I don't like public speaking very much, so I was nervous.

For part of my presentation, I had made a few charts and graphs—four total—which I had to display. I propped them up against the chalkboard. They stayed up all through my report, until the very end, when I needed them most. Just as I was pointing to the first graph, it fell down. I managed to keep my cool as I picked it up, but then right as I placed it back on the board, the second one fell down! Some people in the class started to giggle and my face was turning bright red. Then as I leaned down to pick up the second fallen graph, the third one fell! It was awful—the whole class was cracking up!

—Valerie

Chapter Six

Oops!

Do you ever have moments when you wish you could just stop the world and yell, "Do over?" Sometimes, circumstances simply get out of control and, before you know it, something terribly embarrassing has happened to you. Unfortunately, you can't really turn back the hands of time when something humiliating happens, but you *can* take heart by reading these stories about other people's embarrassing incidents!

Watch Your Step!

One afternoon I was with my mom, taking a city bus home after a day of shopping. We had been on our feet all day and I was really tired. As we were approaching our stop, I got up to get my bags together. I thought I had my balance under control, but as you can probably guess, I didn't. The next thing I knew, the bus jerked and I went flying forward. As I fell to the ground, my arms automatically grabbed onto whatever they could— which, unfortunately, was an old man's knees! I was humiliated. When the bus came to a stop, I apologized to the old man. He said it was okay— in fact, it was the best laugh he'd had all week!

—Katie

Hurdler's Stretch

I run the 100-meter hurdles for our track team. I usually do pretty well. However, that wasn't the case at a meet a couple of weeks ago. I was distracted because this guy I have a big crush on was watching us. He made me very nervous; so much so that, as I was trying to clear the last hurdle, I caught my trailing leg on the top of it. I went sprawling down on the ground—and was disqualified! I didn't get hurt, but I was totally humiliated!

—Denise

Green Goo

I have a baby-sitter named Karen who is totally cool. Last week when she was sitting for me, Karen gave me a beauty makeover. She shampooed my hair, painted my nails, and gave me this green goo to wear on my face overnight. "But don't forget to wash it off in the morning!" she said as she tucked me in for bed. "Of course I won't forget," I remember thinking as I fell asleep. Yeah, right. The next morning, I woke up really late and had to get ready for school in record time. I had only seconds to wash my face and brush my teeth. When I got to school, I noticed a couple of people staring at me, but I didn't have time to check myself out in front of the mirror before class started. By the time I sat down and class began, I knew something was very wrong. I could feel everyone's eyes on me. I asked my friend next to me what was up, and she said, "Your neck is green!" I excused myself from class, ran to the bathroom, and sure enough, there was green gunk all over my neck!

—Natalie

Sewn Up!

One day during arts and crafts, we were learning how to sew. The teacher divided us up into teams to work, one guy and one girl on each team. I really lucked out because I was paired with David, this boy I have a total crush on. During one class, we were supposed to be making aprons. We'd done the basic stuff, and I was sewing a pocket onto the apron. I was having trouble concentrating, however, because of my crush. Before I knew it, I'd sewn the pocket onto the sleeve of my shirt! I felt so stupid and David couldn't stop laughing at me. He didn't stop teasing me for days!

—Cathy

Girl's Best Friend?

I had recently made a new girlfriend and was really excited when she agreed to come over and hang out at my house. Earlier that week, my family had bought a golden retriever puppy. He was cute, but very young and not yet trained. When my friend arrived, in a bright white dress, I knew disaster was ahead. It had rained earlier in the day, so the walkway and grass were wet. I asked my brother to keep Eaton in the house, but—as usual—he let him out, anyway. Before I could intervene, Eaton came running around the house from the backyard—through the wet grass and mud—and jumped right on my friend! She got dirt all over her bright white outfit. She was a good sport about it—luckily for me, she loves dogs—but I was so embarrassed!

—Martha

White Out

This was the worst! I was running late for school one morning, so I got ready in a big rush. Once I was on the bus, I looked down at the bottom of my black T-shirt and noticed there were white streaks all over it. I realized that in my rush I must have gotten deodorant all over it! Once I got to school, I tried to wash out the stubborn stains, but they wouldn't go away. I had to spend the day sporting white streaks!

—Cali

Chapter Seven

Boys Blush?

Does it sometimes seem as though you and your girlfriends are the only ones who get embarrassed? Do you ever think that guys somehow sail through life, effortlessly avoiding extremely humiliating moments? Trust us, that's just not the way it is. Boys blush just like girls do, and the following embarrassing tales from boys' point of view prove it!

Smash!

The other day I was playing a game of football with my friends. We were winning 28-14. I went out for a long pass. I had run about 13 feet when the quarterback threw the ball my way. No one called out my name to tell me that the ball was on the way toward me, and—slam!—the ball hit me right in the back of the head! I was was so embarrassed. My face was red all over and all my friends were laughing at me. I don't think they threw the ball to me again after that. But on the good side, we still won the game!

—Patrick

Scaredy Nat

I really like this girl, Claire, who lives in my neighborhood. One evening, I was walking home from basketball practice. Practice had run late, so it was already dark. Me and my friends had seen a really scary movie the previous weekend, and I guess I was still a little freaked out. As I was walking down my block, I heard some rustling in the bushes. I nervously looked around, but kept walking. All of a sudden, something jumped out from behind a tree. I couldn't help myself, I just started screaming! Then, I heard someone say, "Nat, it's just me." I looked—it was Claire! She was laughing; I was humiliated!

—Nat

Mer-boy

This is the most embarrassing, humiliating thing that can ever happen to a person. My school has an indoor pool, and all students are required to take swimming lessons. I'm a pretty good swimmer; in fact, during one class, the teacher asked me to demonstrate the butterfly. I was concentrating on making perfect, powerful strokes, and didn't notice that my swimming trunks were slowly coming off. It was only when I got to the end of the pool that I realized that my bathing suit had slipped all the way down to my ankles! I quickly turned around, faced the wall, and pulled my trunks back up. But it was too late—everyone had seen my most embarrassing moment. The whole class was was cracking up—even my teacher was laughing! It was the worst moment ever. Now I'm known around school as mer-boy!

—Geoff

Chapter Eight

All-around Embarrassing!

The thing about embarrassing incidents is that you never know when or where they will strike. There's no way to predict when one will occur. The following stories are embarrassing across the board. Whether something similar has happened to you or you just want a laugh, you're sure to enjoy the following selection of totally traumatic tales.

Pillow Problem

One night, I was sleeping over at my best friend's house. At home, I always sleep with two pillows; however, I didn't want to be an annoying guest, so I settled for one. The next morning at breakfast, my pal's parents looked at me with a smile and asked if I enjoyed my pillow. I had no idea what they were talking about! Turns out that I had gotten up in the middle of the night, walked into their room, and asked them for a pillow! I didn't even remember it.

—Cara

Messy Mucus

I have really bad allergies, so I always have a very runny nose. One night, I was out to dinner with my family. I was so used to my nose running all the time that I guess I didn't notice that a stream of snot had slid out of my nostril. Everyone was staring at me, but no one said anything. Finally my brother piped up. "Brie," he said, "please blow your nose. It's grossing everyone out!" Naturally I was mortified, and I was made fun of that whole night! My mom even had our waiter bring over a box of tissues! It was terrible!

—Brie

Plant Problem

One day, I was sitting on my front porch, waiting for my friend and her mom to come get me. They were picking me up to take me to a friend's birthday party. On my porch, we have a lot of plants—my mom loves them. When my ride came, I reached down to get my duffel bag and snagged my hair on a huge asparagus fern. It hurt a bit but I managed to pull my hair free and ran to the car. I did notice my friend and her mom look at me kind of funny, but I ignored it. But when I got to the party, I couldn't ignore the fact that everyone was staring at me. I got totally self-conscious and ran into the bathroom. You can imagine my humiliation when I saw that a dried-out piece of plant was stuck nicely in my hair! I was so embarrassed and upset that no one had told me. When I returned to the party (*without* the piece of plant in my hair), everyone asked why I had taken off my plant hat! Needless to say, I was the butt of most of the jokes that afternoon!

—Gail

Chapter Nine

Trauma-rama!

So there you have it. A whole new collection of blush-inducing stories from kids just like you. Did you recognize yourself in any of the retellings? Just remember, if you feel your face turn bright red and your palms start to sweat, take a few deep breaths and repeat to yourself, "I am not alone." Chances are very good that someone, somewhere, has gone through a similar experience. Take heart: every kid who submitted a story for this book lived through the embarrassment to tell his or her tale!